Materials Needed for File Folder Social Studies Activities

- colored pencils, crayons or watercolor felt markers
- colored construction paper
- self-closing plastic bags or tie-closure manila envelopes
- large paper clips

- scissors
- rubber cement or glue
- file folders (manila or colored)
- tagboard

Guidelines for Construction

1. The two-sided **title tab** allows for quick and easy filing and locating. Copy and cut along the solid lines. Fold along the center dotted line and glue it to the tab on the file folder.
2. Copy the student **game directions**, color as you wish. Cut out and glue to the front of the file folder.
3. Copy the two inside **activity pages** on typing or construction paper. Color as desired. Glue each page to the inside of the file folder. Laminate folder.
4. Copy the **activity pieces** on construction paper. Laminate and cut out. Store in plastic bag or manila envelope.
5. Copy the **answer key** and cut out. Glue it to a piece of tagboard and laminate. Store with activity pieces.

Helpful Hints

You may use file folders with pockets and simply turn the file folder inside out. Store the game pieces and answer key in the back pocket.

Store the completed file folders in a filing cabinet, a filing box, or vertical file tray.

Use file folders . . .

- as a cooperative learning experience.
- as a seatwork assignment.
- as learning center activities.
- as learning tools for working with ESL (English as a Second Language) students.
- as a special activity for those students needing additional practice with a specific skill.
- as a teaching aid when introducing a concept.
- as an activity for those students who complete assignments early.
- as a "choice" during an activity period.

Use evaluation worksheets . . .

(pages 62 - 76)
- as a pre-evaluation of the student's knowledge of a particular skill.
- as a follow-up activity when a student has completed a file folder activity.

Land Ho!

Objective: Identify the correct geographic term for a given definition.

Special Instruction:
May need a map or globe for reference.

Title Tab:

Land Ho!
(geographic terms)

Land Ho!
(geographic terms)

Cut ✂

Land Ho!
(1 Player)

Directions:

- Read each clue.
- Find the matching definition card and place it where it belongs on the puzzle.
- Use the Answer Key to check your work when you are finished.

opy the word cards. Glue to pieces of tagboard. Laminate and cut out along the solid lines.

o	c	e	a	n	p	l	a	i	n	i	s	l	a	n	d	w	e	s	t
A	n	t	a	r	c	t	i	c	a	c	o	n	t	i	n	e	n	t	
S	o	u	t	h	A	m	e	r	i	c	a	e	q	u	a	t	o	r	
A	u	s	t	r	a	l	i	a	p	l	a	t	e	a	u				
s	o	u	t	h															

Copy the Answer Key. Cut out, glue to a piece of tagboard and laminate.

Answer Key

Across

2. Continent southeast of Asia
7. Large body of salt water
8. Flat land that is higher than the land around it
11. Flat land
12. Opposite of north
14. Water is all around this land
17. Map line around the middle of the earth
18. Opposite of east
20. A very large piece of land
25. Continent south of North America
26. Continent at the South Pole

Down

1. Low land between mountains
2. Continent south of Europe
3. A large stream of water
4. Continent east of Europe
5. Water is on three sides of this landform
6. A very high hill
9. Different kinds of land
10. Continent north of South America
13. Continent west of Asia
15. Very dry, sandy land
16. Ocean east of North America
19. Opposite of west
21. Opposite of south
22. Ocean west of North America
23. Raised land smaller than a mountain
24. Water with land all around it.

Naturally Resourceful

Objective: Identify the natural resource used for a given product or activity.

Title Tab:

Naturally Resourceful
(natural resources)

Naturally Resourceful
(natural resources)

Cut

Naturally Resourceful
(1 or 2 Players)

Directions:

for one player

- Read the word on the coal car card.
- Match it to the phrase on a rock to show what that natural resource can be used for.
- Place the coal car card on that rock.
- Use the Answer Key to check your work when you are finished.

for two players

- Stack the coal car cards, word side down, on the activity folder.
- Each player chooses one side of the folder to use.
- Take turns drawing cards and playing.
- If a card cannot be used, place it on the bottom of the stack.
- The winner is the first person to cover his/her side of the folder correctly.

py the coal cards on white construction paper. Laminate and cut out.

tree	water	mineral	mineral

tree	water	mineral	mineral

tree	water	mineral	mineral

tree	water	mineral	mineral

tree	water	mineral	mineral

tree	water	tree	mineral

Answer Key

Copy and enlarge
the Answer Key.
Glue to a piece of
tagboard, cut out
and laminate.

to make
paper

to drink

to make
plastic dishes

to water
crops

to make
tires

to make
a stapler

to make
wooden chairs

to make
jewelry

to make
cars

to fill
a bathtub

to make
paper clips

to make a
wooden
birdhouse

8

to make basketballs

to soak clothes

to make gasoline

to make a wooden dog house

to make plastic toys

to make nails

to make books

to make metal file cabinets

to fill a swimming pool

to make a wooden table

to make tractors

to fill a fish bowl

How Far Is It?

Objective: Measure the distance between given points.

Title Tab:

How Far Is It?
(measuring distance)

How Far Is It?
(measuring distance)

Cut

How Far Is It?
(1 Player)

Directions:

- Place the map and ruler beside the folder.
- Place the suitcase cards above the folder.
- Read a question on the activity folder.
- Use the ruler to measure the distance on the map. (1 inch = 1 mile)
- Find the suitcase with the correct answer and place it after the question.
- Then look at the number of miles and the letters on the cars to know which tires to use to solve the secret code on the folder.
- Use the Answer Key to check your work when you are finished.

opy the Answer Keys. Glue them to pieces of tagboard. Cut out and laminate.

t r a v e l

t	r	a	v	e	l
9 miles	5 miles	4 miles	12 miles	2 miles	7 miles

t h e

t	h	e
9 miles	1 miles	2 miles

d i s t a n c e

d	i	s	t	a	n	c	e
8 miles	10 miles	6 miles	9 miles	4 miles	3 miles	11 miles	2 miles

How far is it from . . .

a 4 miles
d 8 miles
n 3 miles
e 2 miles
t 9 miles
h 1 mile
l 7 miles
i 10 miles
r 5 miles
c 11 miles
s 6 miles
v 12 miles

1. home to Get Some Gas?

2. Get Some Gas to the Dinosaur Museum?

3. the Dinosaur Museum to Rapid Waterfalls?

4. the Glass-Bottom Boat to the Cave Tour?

5. Miniature Golf to Whale Watching to Campers' Campsite?

6. Whale Watching to the Hot Dog Hut?

7. Campers' Campsite to the Ice Cream Parlor?

8. the Ice Cream Parlor to Campers' Campsite to Whale Watching?

9. the Dinosaur Museum to Rapid Waterfalls to the Hot Dog Hut to Whale Watching?

10. Whale Watching to Miniature Golf to the Cave Tour?

11. the Hot Dog Hut to the Glass-Bottom Boat to the Cave Tour?

12. Get Some Gas to the Cave Tour to Miniature Golf to the Ice Cream Parlor?

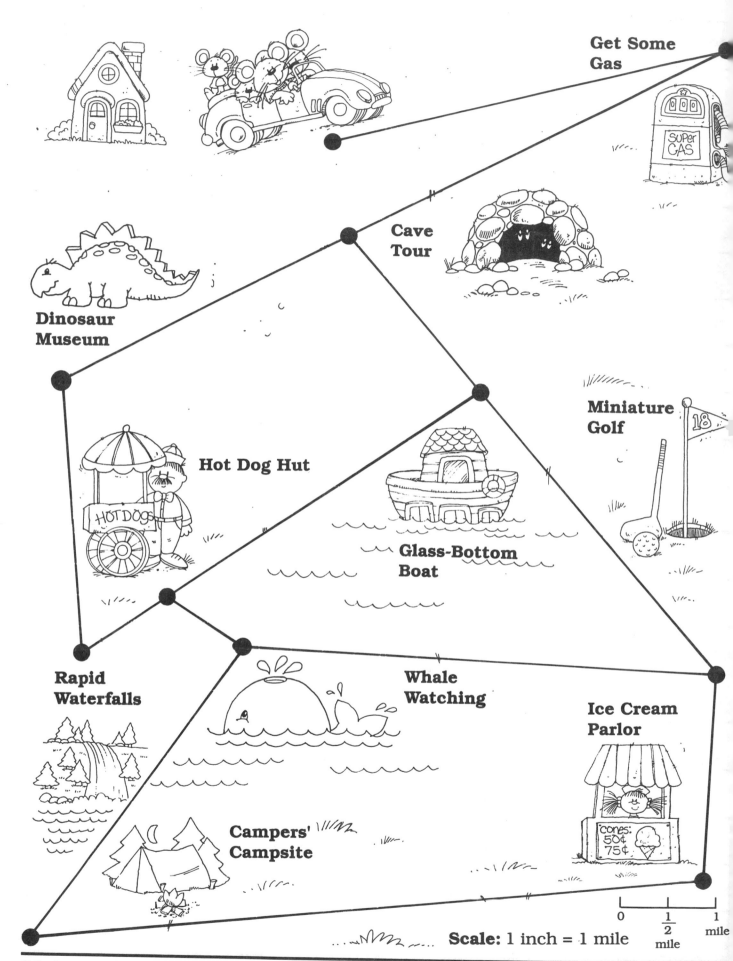

Get Some Gas

Cave Tour

Dinosaur Museum

Miniature Golf

Hot Dog Hut

Glass-Bottom Boat

HOT DOGS

Rapid Waterfalls

Whale Watching

Ice Cream Parlor

Campers' Campsite

cones: 50¢ 75¢

SUPER GAS

18

0   ½   1
     mile mile

Scale: 1 inch = 1 mile

Copy the ruler on yellow construction paper. Laminate and cut out.

4 miles   8 miles   3 miles   2 miles

9 miles   1 mile   7 miles   10 miles

5 miles   11 miles   6 miles   12 miles

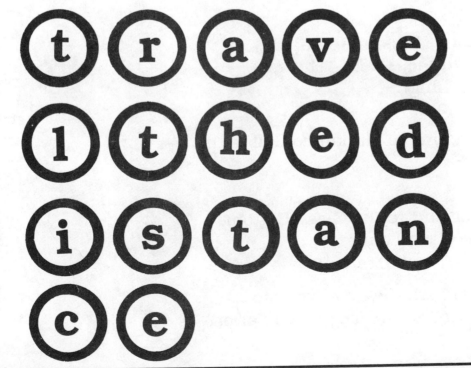

t r a v e
l t h e d
i s t a n
c e

IF8582 File Folder Social Studies Activities

How far is it from . . .

1. home to Get Some Gas?

2. Get Some Gas to the Dinosaur Museum?

3. the Dinosaur Museum to Rapid Waterfalls?

4. the Glass-Bottom Boat to the Cave Tour?

5. Miniature Golf to Whale Watching to Campers' Campsite?

6. Whale Watching to the Hot Dog Hut?

7. Campers' Campsite to the Ice Cream Parlor?

8. the Ice Cream Parlor to Campers' Campsite to Whale Watching?

9. the Dinosaur Museum to Rapid Waterfalls to the Hot Dog Hut to Whale Watching?

10. Whale Watching to Miniature Golf to the Cave Tour?

11. the Hot Dog Hut to the Glass-Bottom Boat to the Cave Tour?

12. Get Some Gas to the Cave Tour to Miniature Golf to the Ice Cream Parlor?

9 miles	5 miles	4 miles	12 miles	2 miles	7 miles

9 miles	1 miles	2 miles

8 miles	10 miles	6 miles	9 miles	4 miles	3 miles	11 miles	2 miles !

"Good Service" Delivery

Objective: Identify which occupations provide goods and which provide services.

Title Tab:

"Good Service" Delivery
(goods and services)

"Good Service" Delivery
(goods and services)

Cut ✂

"Good Service" Delivery
(2 Players)

Directions:

- Pick the game you wish to play.
- Stack the goods and services game cards, word side down, on the delivery truck.
- One player chooses **X**'s and the other chooses **O**'s to use as markers.
- Players take turns drawing game cards and placing them on words from each category.
- Then place your marker (**X** or **O**) on top of the card.
- The first player to mark three **X**'s or **O**'s in a row is the winner. The rows may run across, down or diagonally.
- Use the Answer Key to check your work when you are finished.

Copy two sets of the game cards on light blue construction paper. Laminate and cut out.

Copy the markers on white construction paper. Laminate and cut out.

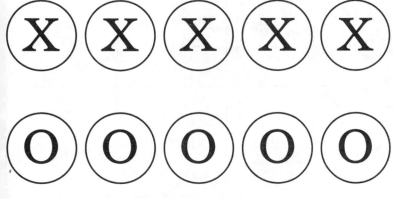

Copy and enlarge the Answer Keys. Cut out, glue to pieces of tagboard and laminate.

grocer	miner	car dealer
barber	bus driver	farmer
police officer	jeweler	nurse

Game 1

Game 2

teacher	pet store owner	mail carrier
florist	doctor	bank teller
firefighter	photog- rapher	artist

Game 3

tailor	baker	telephone operator
farmer	fisherman	clothing manufacturer
cabinet maker	librarian	pilot

Game 4

candy maker	cab driver	bookkeeper
cannery worker	bookstore owner	housekeeper
news reporter	rancher	car repairman

Selecting Supplies

Objective: Identify a given item as a want or a need.

Title Tab:

Selecting Supplies
(wants and needs)

Selecting Supplies
(wants and needs)

Cut ✂

Selecting Supplies
(1 or 2 Players)

Directions:

for one player

- Read the word on a wagon wheel card.
- Find a word in a circle on the folder that names an item belonging in that category.
- Place the wagon wheel card on that circle.
- Use the Answer Key to check your work when you are finished.

for two players

- Stack the wagon wheel cards, word side down, on the activity folder.
- Each player chooses one side of the folder to use.
- Take turns drawing cards and playing.
- If a card cannot be used, place it on the bottom of the stack.
- The winner is the first person to cover his/her side of the folder correctly.

Copy the wagon wheel cards on tan construction paper. Laminate and cut out.

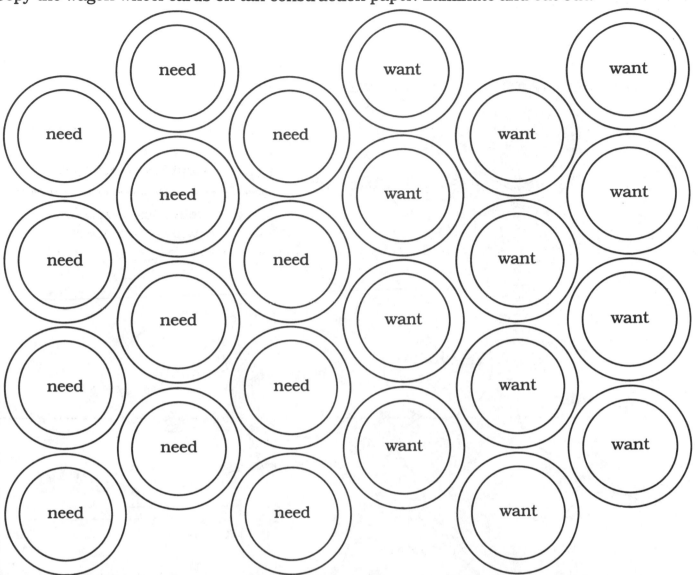

Copy the Answer Key. Glue to a piece of tagboard. Laminate and cut out.

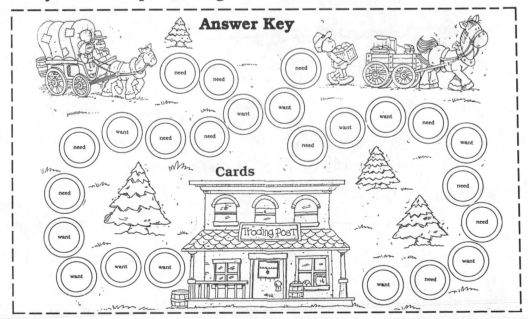

shirt

bread

skateboard

television

fruit

socks

milk

coat

kite

Cards

game

teddy bear

vacation

house

radio

pet

baseball

shoes

water

bike

eggs

pants

necklace

scooter

vegetables

ng POST

APPLE 1¢

Seeking the Sights

Objective: Read and follow directions to place pictures on the correct states.

Title Tab:

Seeking the Sights
(geography)

Seeking the Sights
(geography)

Cut

Seeking the Sights
(1 or 2 Players)

Directions:

for one player

- Choose Sightseeing Tour **1** or **2**.
- Find the correct directions to follow.
- Place all of the picture cards face up.
- Read each direction carefully.
- Place the picture cards where the tour directions tell you.
- Use the Answer Key to check your work when you are finished.

for two players

- Each player chooses one of the Sightseeing Tours to use and then follows the directions for one player.

Copy the Answer Key. Glue it to a piece of tagboard. Laminate and cut out.

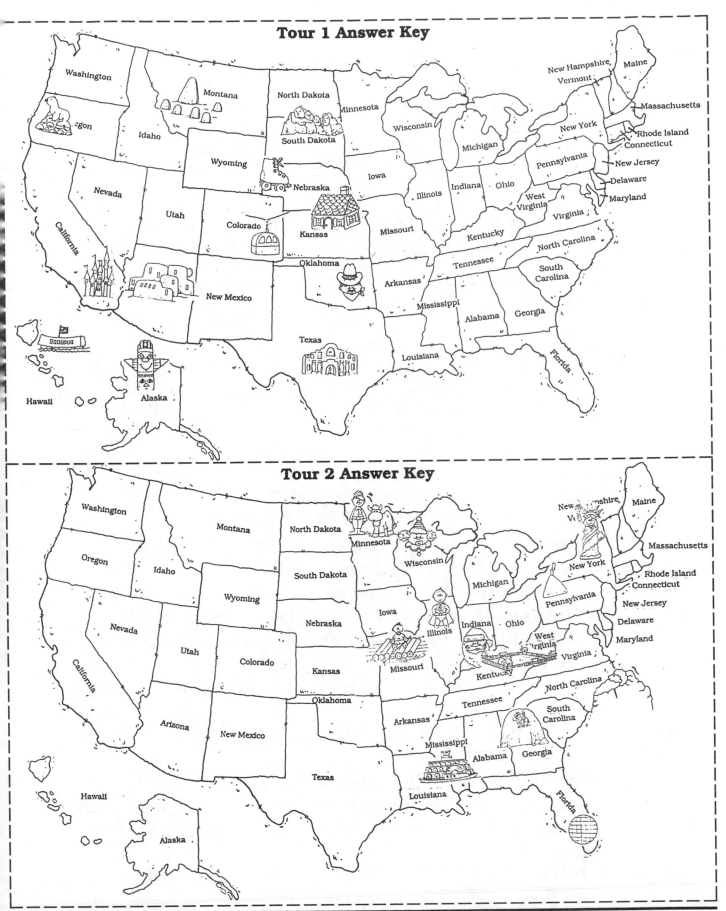

Tour 1 Answer Key

Tour 2 Answer Key

Copy the picture cards on white construction paper. Write **1** on the back of each. Color, laminate and cut out. Store in a plastic bag with corresponding Sightseeing Tour card.

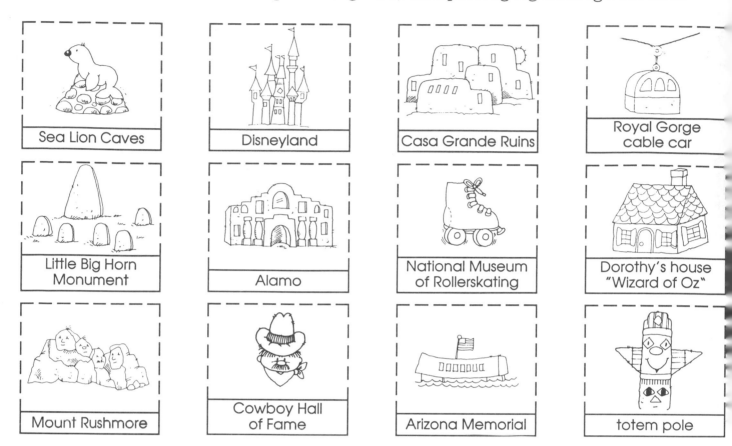

Copy the Sightseeing Tour directions. Glue to a piece of tagboard, cut out and laminate.

Sightseeing Directions – Tour 1

1. Place the **Sea Lion Caves** in the state south of Washington.
2. Place **Disneyland** in the state west of Nevada.
3. Place the **Casa Grande Ruins** in the state south of Utah.
4. Place the **Royal Gorge Cable Car** in the state north of New Mexico.
5. Place the **Little Big Horn Monument** in the state west of North Dakota.
6. Place the **Alamo** in the state south of Oklahoma.
7. Place the symbol for the **National Museum of Rollerskating** in the state north of Kansas.
8. Place **Dorothy's house** from "The Wizard of Oz" in the state west of Missouri.
9. Place **Mount Rushmore** in the state south of North Dakota.
10. Place the symbol for the **Cowboy Hall of Fame** in the state west of Arkansas.
11. Place the **Arizona Memorial** on the state made of islands southwest of California.
12. Place the **totem pole** in the state that is really northwest of Washington.

Copy the picture cards on white construction paper. Write **2** on the back of each. Color, laminate and cut out. Store in a plastic bag with corresponding Sightseeing Tour card.

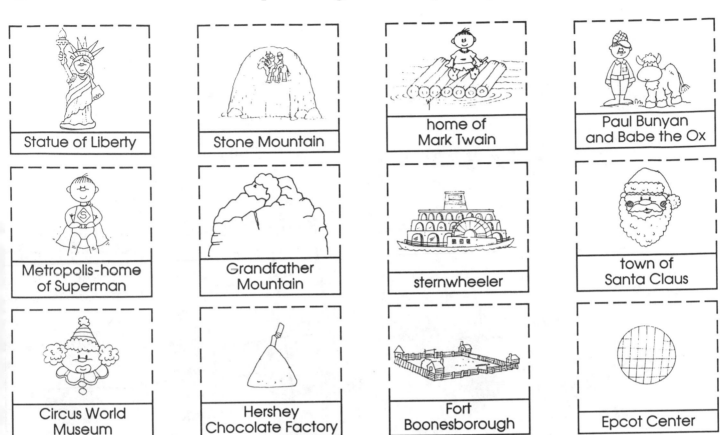

Copy the Sightseeing Tour directions. Glue to a piece of tagboard, cut out and laminate.

Sightseeing Directions – Tour 2

1. Place the **Statue of Liberty** in the state north of Pennsylvania.
2. Place the symbol for the **Hershey Chocolate Factory** in the state east of Ohio and north of West Virginia.
3. Place the symbol for the town of **Santa Claus** in the state west of Ohio.
4. Place **Paul Bunyan and Babe the Blue Ox** in the state north of Iowa.
5. Place the symbol for **Metropolis – Home of Superman** in the state east of Iowa and Missouri.
6. Place the **sternwheeler** in the state west of Alabama.
7. Place the symbol for the home of **Mark Twain** in the state east of Kansas.
8. Place the symbol for the **Circus World Museum** in the state west of Michigan.
9. Place **Fort Boonesborough** in the state north of Tennessee.
10. Place **Grandfather Mountain** in the state south of Virginia.
11. Place the **Epcot Center** in the state south of Alabama and Georgia.
12. Place **Stone Mountain** in the state east of Alabama.

Briefly Addressed

Objective: Identify the correct postal abbreviation for each state.

Special Note: Use the United States map on pages 28 and 29 for the gameboard for this activity.

Cut ✂

Title Tab:

(state name abbreviations)
Briefly Addressed

Briefly Addressed
(state name abbreviations)

Briefly Addressed
(1 or 2 Players)

Directions:

for one player

- Place the mail truck cards around the folder.
- Pick a mail truck card with a state's abbreviation on it.
- Find the state outline on the map gameboard.
- Place the mail truck card on that state.
- Use the Answer Key to check your work when you are finished.

for two players

- Stack the mail truck cards near the folder.
- Take turns drawing cards and playing.

Copy and enlarge the Answer Key. Glue to a piece of tagboard, cut out and laminate.

Answer Key

Copy the mail truck game pieces on white construction paper. Laminate and cut out.

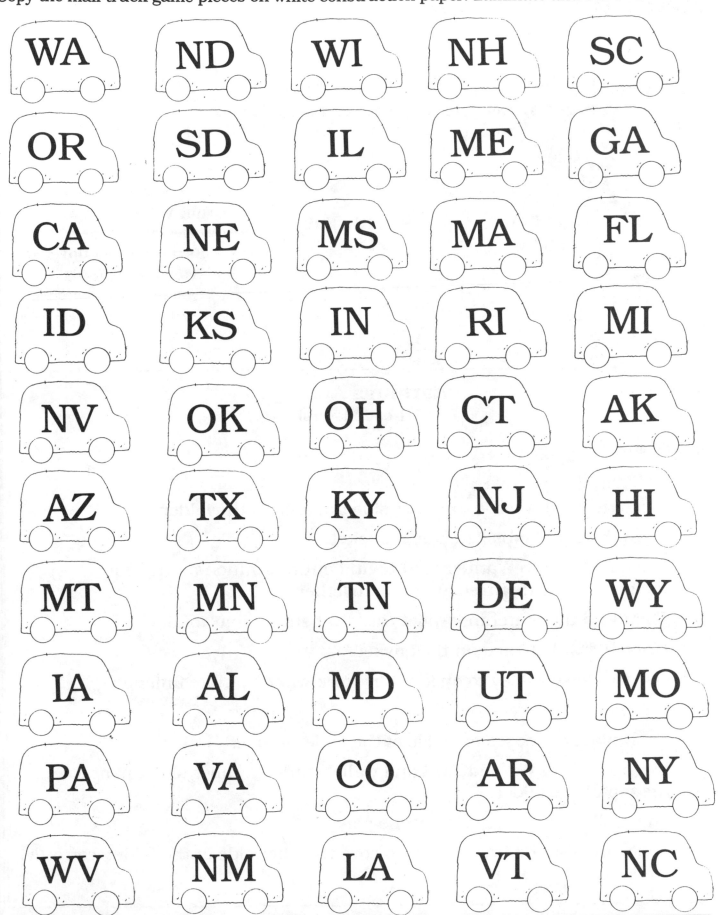

WA ND WI NH SC
OR SD IL ME GA
CA NE MS MA FL
ID KS IN RI MI
NV OK OH CT AK
AZ TX KY NJ HI
MT MN TN DE WY
IA AL MD UT MO
PA VA CO AR NY
WV NM LA VT NC

Earnings Add Up!

Objective: Identify the total amount of money earned for three given jobs.

Special Directions: Keep scrap paper and pencils with folder for students to use.

Title Tab:

(earning money)
Earnings Add Up!

Earnings Add Up!
(earning money)

Cut ✂

Earnings Add Up!
(1 or 2 Players)

Directions:

for one player

- Place the wallet cards, number side up, around the folder.
- Read the set of jobs listed on a basket.
- Look at the Help Wanted card to find out how much money each job pays. Add the three amounts together.
- Then find the matching wallet card that shows that total.
- Place the wallet card on the basket.
- Use the Answer Key to check your work when you are finished.

for two players

- Each player chooses one side of the folder to use.
- Place the Help Wanted card and wallet cards, number side up, at the top of the folder.
- Then follow the directions for one player.
- The winner is the first person to cover his/her side of the folder correctly.

Copy the Help Wanted card and glue it to a piece of tagboard. Laminate and cut out.

Help Wanted

Rake leaves $2.50	Pick strawberries $3.25	Sweep floor $1.00
Vacuum rugs $1.75	Feed fish $.85	Wash dog $2.25

Copy the wallet cards on orange construction paper. Laminate and cut out.

$6.75 $7.50 $6.60 $8.00 $5.60 $5.25 $4.35

$5.75 $4.10 $5.85 $7.25 $3.60

$4.85 $5.00

Copy and enlarge the Answer Key. Cut out, glue to piece of tagboard and laminate.

Answer Key

$7.25 — vacuum rugs, pick strawberries, wash dog
$6.75 — sweep floor, pick strawberries, rake leaves
$5.60 — feed fish, wash dog, rake leaves
$7.50 — vacuum rugs, rake leaves, pick strawberries
$4.10 — sweep floor, feed fish, wash dog
$3.60 — feed fish, vacuum rugs, sweep floor
$6.60 — feed fish, rake leaves, pick strawberries
$5.85 — feed fish, pick strawberries, vacuum rugs
$5.00 — vacuum rugs, sweep floor, wash dog
$4.85 — wash dog, feed fish, vacuum rugs
$4.35 — sweep floor, rake leaves, feed fish
$8.00 — wash dog, pick strawberries, rake leaves
$5.75 — sweep floor, rake leaves, wash dog
$5.25 — sweep floor, vacuum rugs, rake leaves

vacuum rugs
pick strawberries
wash dog

sweep floor
pick strawberries
rake leaves

sweep floor
feed fish
wash dog

feed fish
rake leaves
pick strawberries

vacuum rugs
sweep floor
wash dog

sweep floor
rake leaves
feed fish

wash dog
pick strawberries
rake leaves

34

feed fish
wash dog
rake leaves

vacuum rugs
rake leaves
pick strawberries

feed fish
vacuum rugs
sweep floor

feed fish
pick strawberries
vacuum rugs

wash dog
feed fish
vacuum rugs

sweep floor
rake leaves
wash dog

sweep floor
vacuum rugs
rake leaves

So Many Choices!

Objective: Identify the possible combinations of items that may be purchased with a given amount of money.

Cut ✂

Title Tab:

So Many Choices!
(spending money)

So Many Choices!
(spending money)

So Many Choices!
(1 or 2 Players)

Directions:

for one player

- Choose one side of the folder on which to play. (**Pampered Pets** or **Art Corner**)

- Place the matching price tag cards around the folder.

- Check the amount of money the child has to spend.

- Look at the cost of each item.

- Find seven sets of three price tags whose prices together equal the total amount the child can spend. Place them on the folder. Each set must be different.

- Use the Answer Key to check your work when you are finished. (Your answers may be in a different order.)

for two players

- Each player chooses one side of the activity folder to use.

- Follow the directions for one player.

Enlarge the Answer Keys. Cut out, glue to pieces of tagboard and laminate.

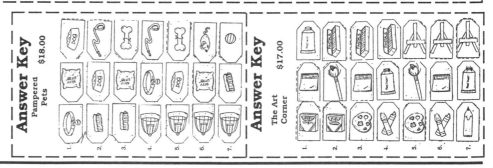

Copy the price tag cards for Pampered Pets on yellow construction paper. Write **Pampered Pets** on the back of each. Laminate and cut out. Store in a separate plastic bag.

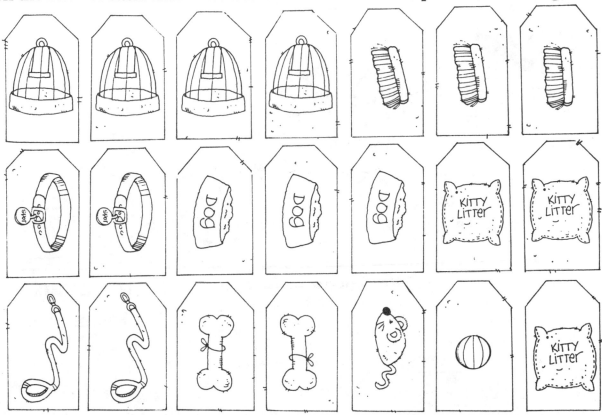

Copy the price tag cards for the Art Corner on green construction paper. Write **Art Corner** on the back of each. Laminate and cut out. Store in a separate plastic bag.

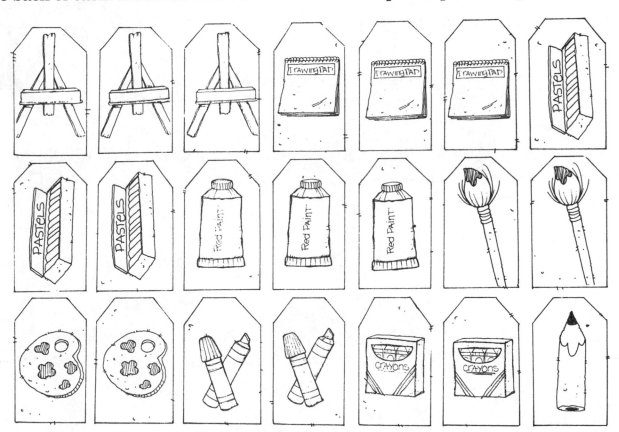

Pampered Pets

1.

2.

3.

4.

5.

6.

7.

$18.00

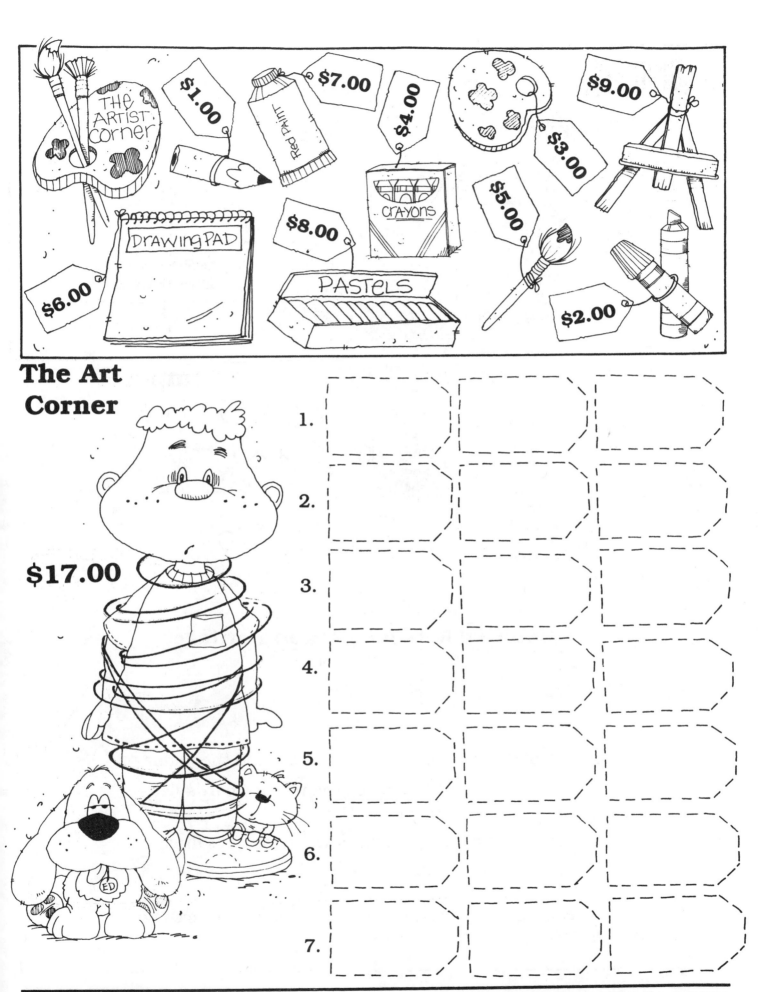

The Art Corner

$17.00

1.

2.

3.

4.

5.

6.

7.

Exhibiting Native American Heritage

Objective: Follow directions to correctly identify Native American cultures.

Title Tab:

(Native Americans)
Exhibiting Native American Heritage

Exhibiting Native American Heritage
(Native Americans)

Cut ✂

Exhibiting Native American Heritage
(1 or 2 Players)

Directions:

for one player

- Place all the picture cards, picture side up, around the folder.
- Read the Display Directions and place the picture cards where they belong on the activity folder.
- Use the Answer Key to check your work when you are finished.

for two players

- Take turns reading the directions and placing the pictures where they belong on the activity folder.

Copy the picture cards on construction paper. Color, laminate and cut out.

Cheyenne

Mohawk

Shoshoni

Seminole

Navajo

Tlingit

buffalo-hide tepee

long house

buffalo-hide tepee

Haida plank house

hogan

chickee

Copy the picture cards on construction paper. Color, laminate and cut out.

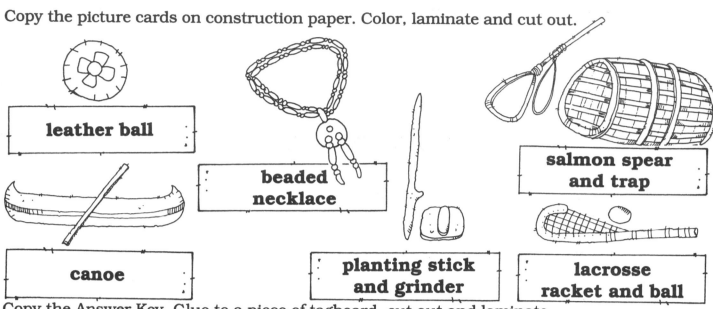

leather ball

beaded necklace

salmon spear and trap

canoe

planting stick and grinder

lacrosse racket and ball

Copy the Answer Key. Glue to a piece of tagboard, cut out and laminate.

Answer Key

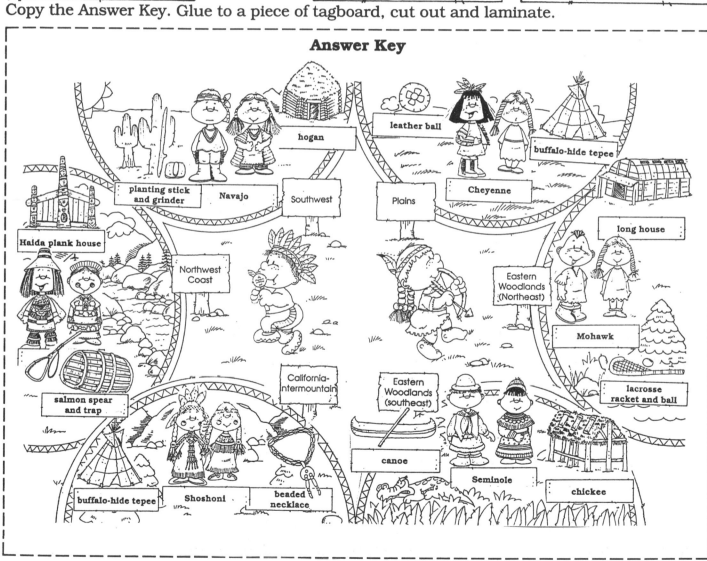

hogan

leather ball

buffalo-hide tepee

planting stick and grinder

Navajo

Southwest

Plains

Cheyenne

Haida plank house

long house

Northwest Coast

Eastern Woodlands (Northeast)

Mohawk

salmon spear and trap

California-Intermountain

Eastern Woodlands (southeast)

lacrosse racket and ball

canoe

buffalo-hide tepee

Shoshoni

beaded necklace

Seminole

chickee

Copy the Display Directions. Glue it to a piece of tagboard, laminate and cut out.

Display Directions

1. Place the Cheyenne girl and boy in the middle of the Plains display.

2. Place the Shoshoni boy and girl in the middle of the California-Intermountain display.

3. Place the Mohawk girl and boy in the middle of the Eastern Woodlands (Northeast) display.

4. Place the Tlingit boy and girl in the middle of the Northwest Coast display.

5. Place the Seminole girl and boy in the middle of the Eastern Woodlands (Southeast) display.

6. Place the Navajo boy and girl in the middle of the Southwest display.

7. Place the long house in the display north of the Seminole and south of the Cheyenne.

8. Place the hogan in the display north of the Tlingit.

9. Place the chickee in the display south of the Mohawks.

10. Place the Haida plank house in the display north of the Shoshoni.

11. Place one buffalo tepee in the display north of the Mohawks.

12. Place the other buffalo tepee in the display south of the Mohawk.

13. Place the salmon spear and trap in the display south of the Navajo.

14. Place the leather ball in the display east of the Navajo.

15. Place the beaded necklace in the display west of the Seminole.

16. Place the canoe in the display south of the Mohawk.

17. Place the planting stick and grinder in the display north of the Tlingit.

18. Place the lacrosse racket and ball in the display north of the Seminole and south of the Cheyenne.

Southwest

Northwest Coast

California-Intermountain

Plains

Eastern
Woodlands
(Northeast)

Eastern
Woodlands
(southeast)

Proudly Praising Our Country

Objective: Place pictures on a grid according to given directions.

Cut ✂

Title Tab:

(U.S. symbols and places)
Proudly Praising Our Country

Proudly Praising Our Country
(U.S. symbols and places)

Proudly Praising Our Country
(1 or 2 Players)

Directions:

for one player

- Choose the grid you want to use – **1** or **2**.
- Find the correct directions to follow.
- Place all the picture cards face up.
- Read each direction carefully and place the picture card where the it tells you to.
- Use the Answer Key to check your work when you are finished.

for two players

- Each player may choose a grid to use and then follow the directions for one player.

Enlarge the Answer Keys. Glue to pieces of tagboard, cut out and laminate.

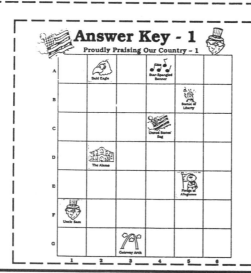

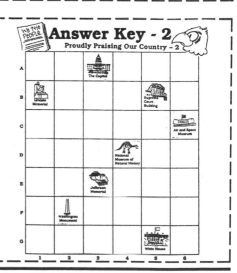

Copy each set of picture cards on a different color of construction paper and write the set number on the back. Color, laminate and cut out. Store each set in a separate plastic bag.

Cards for 1

Cards for 2

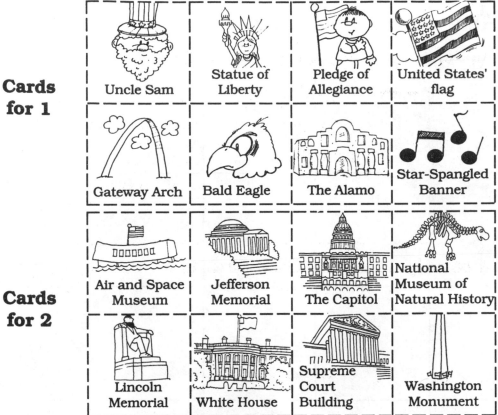

Copy each direction card on white construction paper. Glue to pieces of tagboard, cut out and laminate. Store in bags with corresponding picture cards.

Proudly Praising Our Country Directions – 1	Proudly Praising Our Country Directions – 2
Go to . . .	Go to . . .
F1. Place Uncle Sam here.	**C6**. Place the Air & Space Museum here.
B5. Place the Statue of Liberty here.	**E3**. Place the Jefferson Memorial here.
E5. Place the Pledge of Allegiance here.	**A3**. Place the Capitol here.
C4. Place the United States' flag here.	**D4**. Place the National Museum of Natural History here.
G3. Place the Gateway Arch here.	**B1**. Place the Lincoln Memorial here.
A2. Place the bald eagle here.	**G5**. Place the White House here.
D2. Place the Alamo here.	**B5**. Place the Supreme Court Building here.
A4. Place the Star-Spangled Banner here.	**F2**. Place the Washington Monument here.

Proudly Praising Our Country – 1

	1	2	3	4	5	6
A						
B						
C						
D						
E						
F						
G						

Proudly Praising Our Country – 2

	1	2	3	4	5	6
A						
B						
C						
D						
E						
F						
G						

"Time"-ly Toy Gifts

Objective: Use a time line to answer questions.

Special Construction Directions:

1. Insert brads in each of the 17 circles next to the words/numbers on page 53.

2. Cut a piece of yarn 42" long. Tie one end of the yarn to the brad in the dark circle.

Cut ✂

Title Tab:

"Time"-ly Toy Gifts
(time line)

"Time"-ly Toy Gifts
(time line)

"Time"-ly Toy Gifts
(1 Player)

Directions:

- Place the time line at the top of the folder.

- Read a question on the folder.

- Find the gift card that has the correct answer on it and place it next to the question.

- When you are finished, use the yarn to connect the puzzle dots in the same order as your answers.

- Use the Answer Keys to check your work.

Copy and enlarge the Answer Keys. Glue to pieces of tagboard, cut out and laminate.

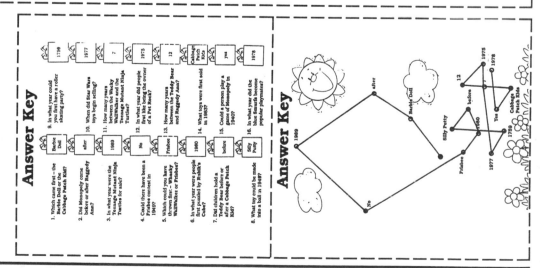

Copy the time line on yellow construction paper. Cut out, glue the sections together and laminate.

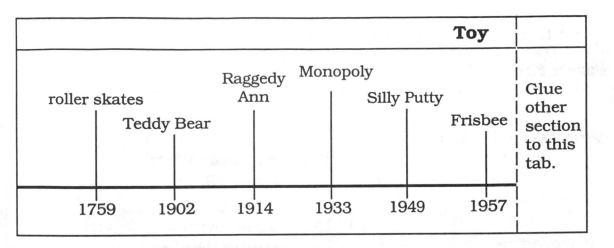

						Toy		

roller skates | Teddy Bear | Raggedy Ann | Monopoly | Silly Putty | Frisbee

Glue other section to this tab.

1759   1902   1914   1933   1949   1957

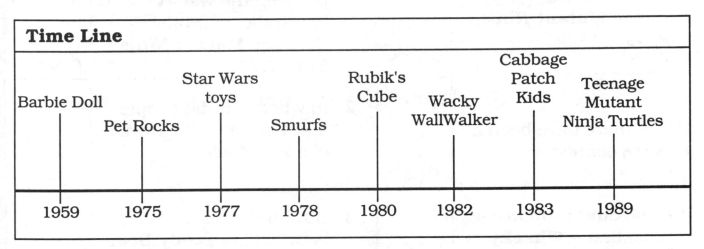

Time Line

Barbie Doll | Pet Rocks | Star Wars toys | Smurfs | Rubik's Cube | Wacky WallWalker | Cabbage Patch Kids | Teenage Mutant Ninja Turtles

1959   1975   1977   1978   1980   1982   1983   1989

Copy gift cards on bright construction paper. Laminate and cut out.

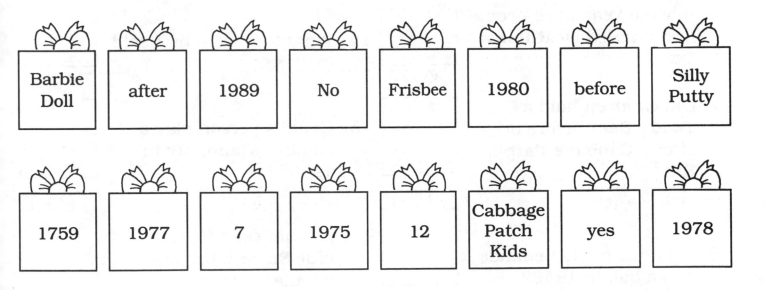

Barbie Doll	after	1989	No	Frisbee	1980	before	Silly Putty
1759	1977	7	1975	12	Cabbage Patch Kids	yes	1978

1. Which came first – the **Barbie Doll** or the **Cabbage Patch Kid**?

2. Did **Monopoly** come before or after **Raggedy Ann**?

3. In what year were the **Teenage Mutant Ninja Turtles** for sale?

4. Could there have been a **Frisbee** contest in 1949?

5. Which could you have thrown first – **Whacky WallWalker** or **Frisbee**?

6. In what year were people first puzzled by **Rubik's Cube**?

7. Did children hold a **Teddy Bear** before or after a **Cabbage Patch Kid**?

8. What toy could be made into a ball in 1949?

9. In what year could you first have a roller skating party?

10. When did **Star Wars** toys begin selling?

11. How many years between the **Wacky WallWalker** and the **Teenage Mutant Ninja Turtles**?

12. In what year did people first like being the owner of a **Pet Rock**?

13. How many years between the **Teddy Bear** and **Raggedy Ann**?

14. What toys were first sold in 1983?

15. Could a person play a game of **Monopoly** in 1940?

16. In what year did the blue **Smurfs** become popular playmates?

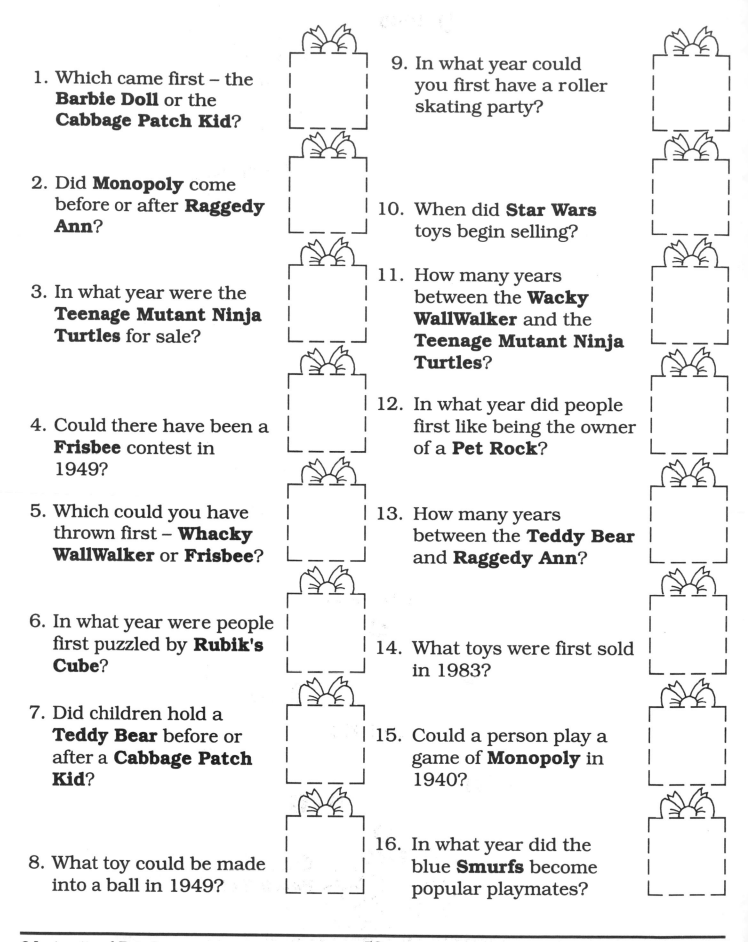

○ 1989

○ No

○ after

○ Barbie Doll

●

Silly Putty
○

Frisbee ○

○ 12

○ before

○ 1980

○ 7   ○ 1975

1977 ○

○ 1978

Yes ○

○

1759

Cabbage
Patch Kids ○

It's Time to Eat

Objective: Place pictures where they belong on a time line according to given information.

Title Tab:

It's Time to Eat
(making a time line)

It's Time to Eat
(making a time line)

Cut

It's Time to Eat
(1 Player)

Directions:

- Place the food picture cards around the folder.
- Read the Time Line Directions.
- Place the pictures in the spaces where they belong on the time line.
- Use the Answer Key to check your work when you are finished.

Copy and enlarge the Answer Key. Glue to a piece of tagboard, cut out and laminate.

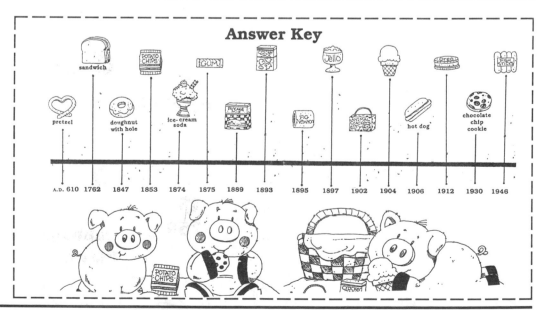

Answer Key

sandwich · pretzel · doughnut with hole · ice-cream soda · POTATO CHIPS · GUM · FIG NEWTON · ANIMAL CRACKERS · Jello · hot dog · chocolate chip cookie · OREO

A.D. 610 1762 1847 1853 1874 1875 1889 1893 1895 1897 1902 1904 1906 1912 1930 1946

Copy the food cards on white construction paper. Color, laminate and cut out.

pretzel **sandwich** **hot dog** **ice- cream soda**

Cracker JACK **Jello** **chocolate chip cookie** **ANIMAL Crackers** **FIG-Newton** **Oreo** **doughnut with hole**

Copy the Time Line Directions on construction paper, cut out and laminate.

Time Line Directions

1. The pretzel was made in the year A.D. 610 as an award for children.

2. The hot dog received its name from a cartoonist in 1906.

3. Animal Crackers were given as presents on Christmas in 1902.

4. Doughnuts with holes first appeared in 1847 to get rid of soggy centers.

5. Sandwiches became popular during the time between pretzels and doughnuts with holes.

6. You could first stir up pancake mix in 1889.

7. Ice-cream cones were sold at a World's Fair 2 years after the Animal Crackers were first sold.

8. You could taste a crispy potato chip 6 years after a hole appeared in a doughnut.

9. Oreos became a favorite 8 years after the ice-cream cone.

10. Ice-cream sodas were first made about 21 years after the potato chip.

11. Chocolate chip cookies were first made after Oreos, but before frozen fish sticks.

12. You could enjoy flavored chewing gum after the ice-cream soda, but before pancake mix.

13. Cracker Jacks were a great snack 4 years after the pancake mix.

14. Wiggly Jell-O could be eaten after Fig Newtons, but before Animal Crackers.

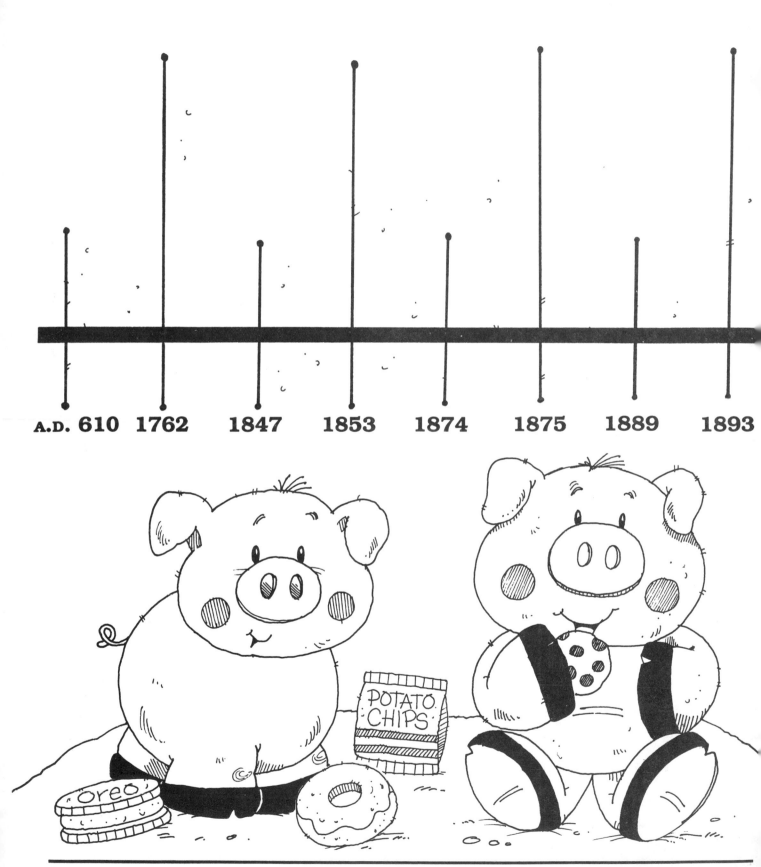

A.D. **610**   **1762**   **1847**   **1853**   **1874**   **1875**   **1889**   **1893**

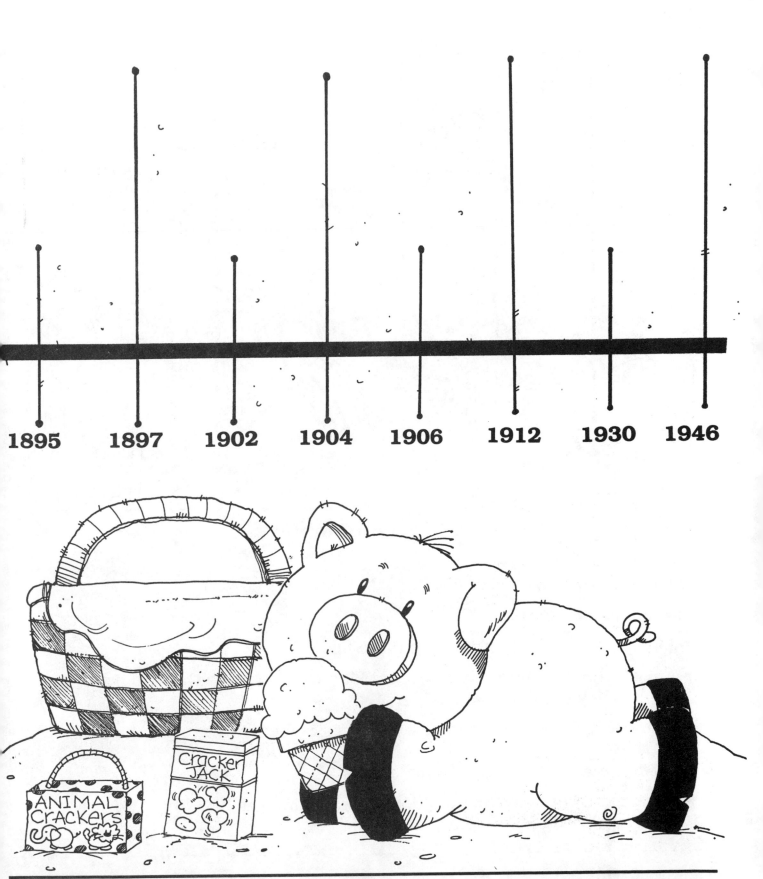

1895   1897   1902   1904   1906   1912   1930   1946

Build a Community

Objective: Follow directions to correctly place buildings where they belong in a given community.

Title Tab:

Build a Community
(community)

Build a Community
(community)

Cut

Build a Community
(1 or 2 Players)

Directions:

for one player

• Place the building cards around the folder.

• Follow the directions on the Town Plan card to place the buildings where they belong on the folder.

• Use the Answer Key to check your work when you are finished.

for two players

• Take turns reading the directions and placing the building cards where they belong.

Copy the building cards on white construction paper. Color, laminate and cut out.

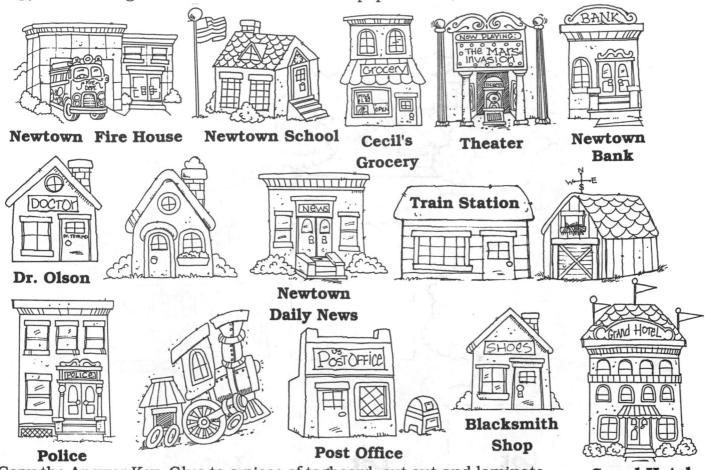

Newtown Fire House **Newtown School** **Cecil's Grocery** **Theater** **Newtown Bank**

Dr. Olson **Newtown Daily News** **Train Station**

Police **Post Office** **Blacksmith Shop** **Grand Hotel**

Copy the Answer Key. Glue to a piece of tagboard, cut out and laminate.

Answer Key

Newtown School

Post Office Newtown Fire House

Cecil's Grocery Theater Grand Hotel Police Blacksmith Shop

Newtown Bank Dr. Olson Newtown Daily News

Train Station

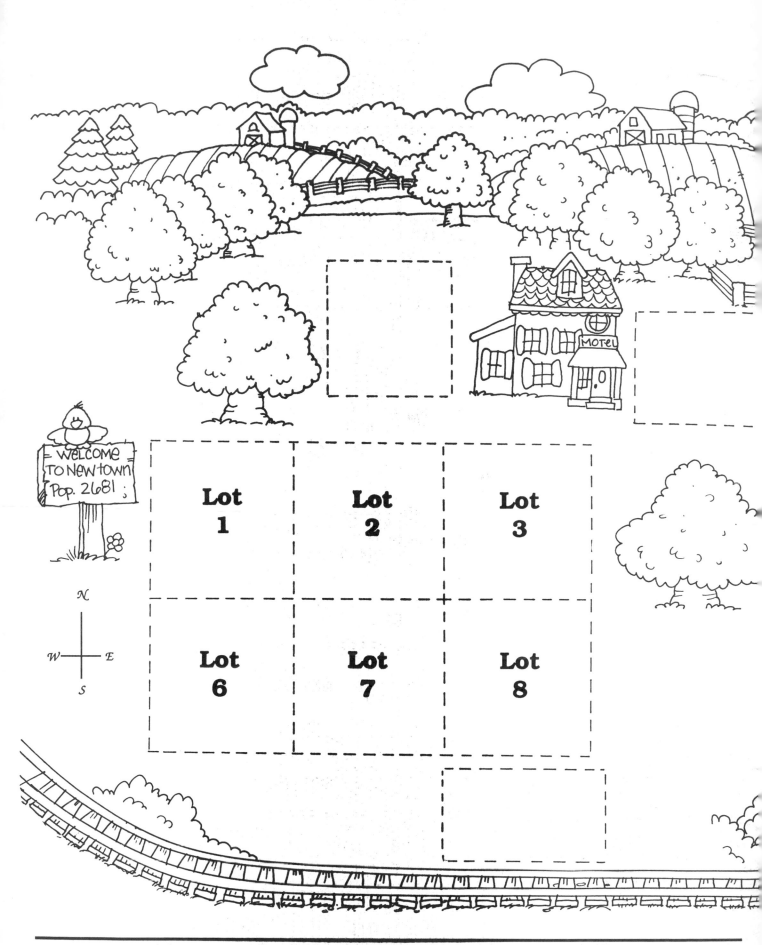

Welcome
TO New town
Pop. 2681

Lot 1

Lot 2

Lot 3

Lot 6

Lot 7

Lot 8

N

W — E

S

MOTEL

Lot
4

Lot
5

Lot
9

Lot
10

Copy the Town Plan card. Glue it to a piece of tagboard. Laminate and cut out.

Town Plan

1. Place the barn **west** of the farmhouse and **east** of the fence.

2. Place the train on the track **northeast** of the tunnel.

3. Place the grocery store in the lot **east** of the town sign and **west** of Lot 2.

4. Place the train station **west** of the stairs and **south** of Lot 8.

5. Place the Fire House in the lot **west** of the town clock and **east** of Lot 4.

6. Place the house **northeast** of the grocery store and **west** of the motel.

7. Place the theater in the lot **south** of the house and **north** of Lot 7.

8. Place the newspaper office in the lot **north** of the train station and **south** of Lot 3.

9. Place the Post Office in the lot **west** of the Fire House, **north** of Lot 9 and east of Lot 3.

10. Place the school **west** of the farm and **east** of the motel.

11. Place the bank in the lot **north** of the train tracks and two lots **west** of the newspaper office.

12. Place the doctor's office in the lot **south** of the theater and **east** of the bank.

13. Place the Blacksmith Shop in the lot **north** of the train tracks, **south** of the Fire House and two lots **east** of the newspaper office.

14. Place the Police Station in the lot **south** of the Post Office and **north** of the stairs.

15. Place the Grand Hotel in the lot **west** of the Post Office and **east** of the theater.

Land Ho!

geographic terms

Name _____

Read each clue. Find the matching word in the Word Bank. Write it in the puzzle.

Across

1. Opposite of south
4. Raised land smaller than mountain
5. Opposite of east
6. A very high hill
10. Water with land all around it
11. Water is on three sides of this landform
12. Opposite of west
14. A very large piece of land

Down

2. Large body of salt water
3. Flat land that is higher than the land around it
7. Water is all around this land
8. Very dry, sandy land
9. A large stream of water
11. Flat land
13. Opposite of north

Word Bank

continent	lake	plain
desert	mountain	plateau
east	north	river
hill	ocean	south
island	peninsula	west

Naturally Resourceful

Name _____

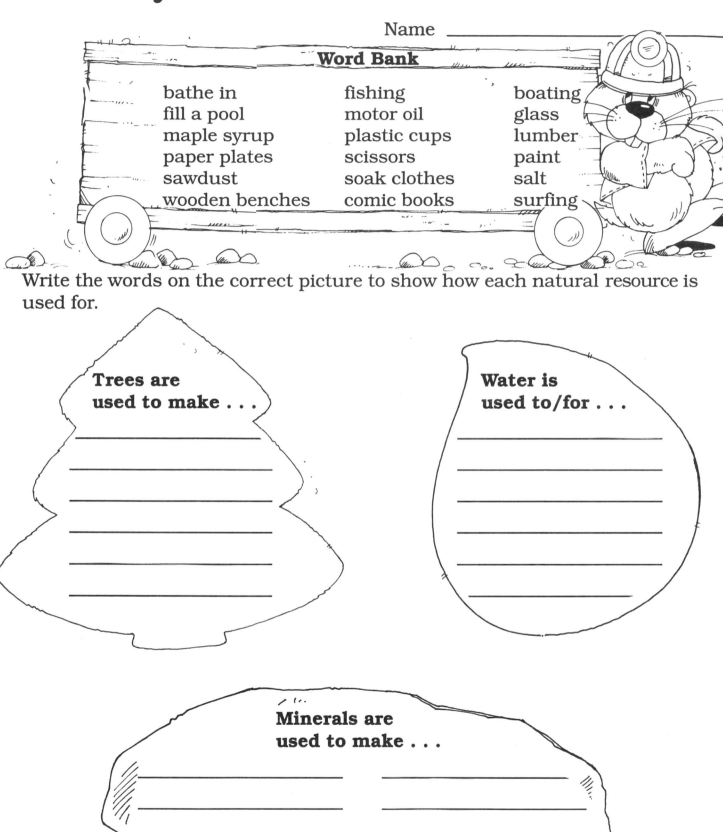

Word Bank

bathe in	fishing	boating
fill a pool	motor oil	glass
maple syrup	plastic cups	lumber
paper plates	scissors	paint
sawdust	soak clothes	salt
wooden benches	comic books	surfing

Write the words on the correct picture to show how each natural resource is used for.

Trees are used to make . . .

Water is used to/for . . .

Minerals are used to make . . .

How Far Is It?

Name _____

Use your ruler to measure each distance on the map. Then use the letters on the tires and your answers to solve the message at the bottom of the page.

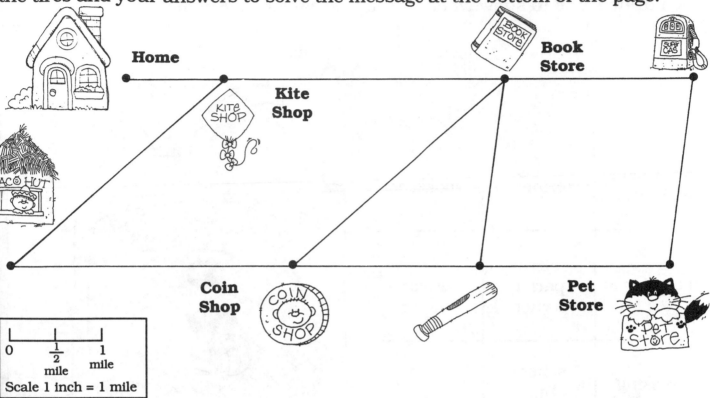

How far is it from . . .

1. home to the Kite Shop? _____ Ⓢ

2. home to the Book Store to the Gas Station? _____ Ⓔ

3. home to the Kite Shop to the Taco Hut? _____ Ⓟ

4. the Taco Hut to the Coin Shop to the Book Store to the Gas Station? _____ Ⓐ

5. the Taco Hut to the Coin Shop? _____ Ⓤ

6. the Baseball Field to the Book Store to the Kite Shop? _____ Ⓓ

7. the Pet Store to the Gas Station? _____ Ⓡ

8. the Gas Station to the Pet Store to the Baseball Field to the Coin Shop to the Taco Hut? _____ Ⓜ

You __ __ __ __ __ __ __ __ __ __ !
    9 6 8 1 3 2 6 5   3 4

"Good Service" Delivery

goods and services

Name _____

Read each word. If it names an occupation that provides goods, mark **G** on the word. If it names an occupation that provides a service, mark **S** on the word. Then draw a line to show where three answers are the same in a row.

television salesperson	veterinarian	zookeeper
receptionist	pizza parlor owner	lawyer
crossing guard	school bus driver	kite manufacturer

actor	plumber	toy maker
firefighter	music store owner	principal
shoe salesperson	cook	babysitter

Selecting Supplies

Name _____

Read each word in the Word Bank. If a word names a **need**, write it on the sack of flour. If a word names a **want**, write it on the pickle barrel.

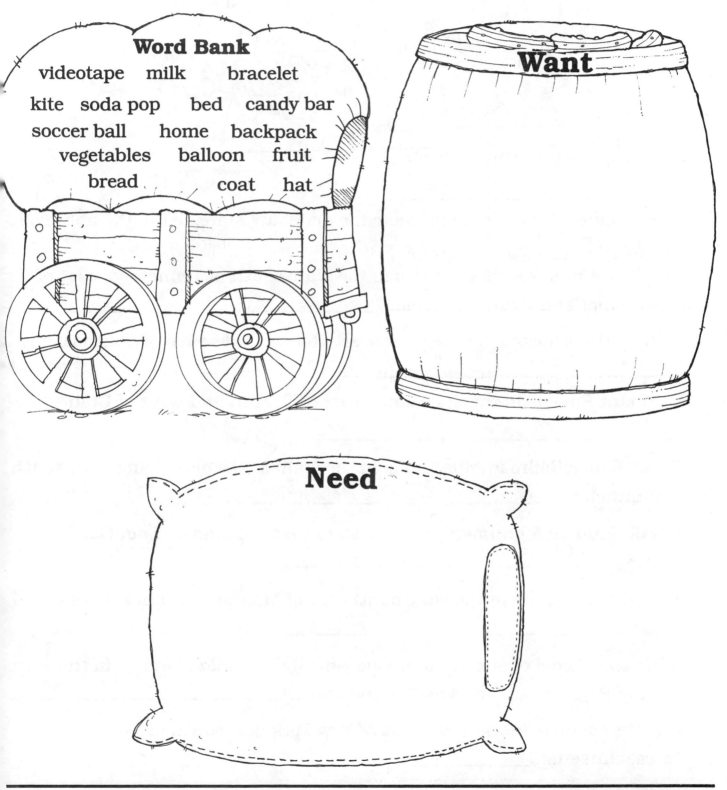

Word Bank

videotape milk bracelet

kite soda pop bed candy bar

soccer ball home backpack

vegetables balloon fruit

bread coat hat

Want

Need

Seeking the Sights

Name _____

Read each clue. Use the map to locate the matching state. Write the abbreviati on on the line.

1. The Space and Rocket Center is in the state south of Tennessee, **east** of Mississippi and **west** of Georgia. _____

2. Buffalo Bill's home is in the state **west** of Iowa and **south** of South Dakota.
_____

3. Elephant Rock is in the state **southeast** of Oregon and **west** of Utah.
_____

4. Casey Jones Railroad Museum is in the state **north** of Alabama and **south** of Kentucky. _____

5. Fossil National Monument is in the state **east** of Idaho and **south** of Montana. _____

6. The Corn Palace is in the state **southeast** of Montana and **northwest** of Iowa. _____

7. A life-size model of one of Columbus' ships, the *Santa Maria*, is in the state **west** of Pennsylvania and **east** of Indiana. _____

8. Gillette Castle is in the state **east** of New York and **south** of Massachusetts. _____

Briefly Addressed

Name _____

Write the postal abbreviation for each state.

1. Washington _____
2. California _____
3. Nevada _____
4. Montana _____
5. Utah _____
6. New Mexico _____
7. South Dakota _____
8. Kansas _____
9. Texas _____
10. Iowa _____
11. Arkansas _____
12. Wisconsin _____
13. Mississippi _____
14. Ohio _____
15. Tennessee _____
16. Pennsylvania _____
17. Vermont _____
18. Maine _____
19. Rhode Island _____
20. New Jersey _____
21. Maryland _____
22. West Virginia _____
23. South Carolina _____
24. Florida _____
25. Alaska _____

26. Oregon _____
27. Idaho _____
28. Arizona _____
29. Wyoming _____
30. Colorado _____
31. North Dakota _____
32. Nebraska _____
33. Oklahoma _____
34. Minnesota _____
35. Missouri _____
36. Louisiana _____
37. Illinois _____
38. Indiana _____
39. Kentucky _____
40. Alabama _____
41. New York _____
42. New Hampshire _____
43. Massachusetts _____
44. Connecticut _____
45. Delaware _____
46. Virginia _____
47. North Carolina _____
48. Georgia _____
49. Michigan _____
50. Hawaii _____

Earnings Add Up!

Name _____

Help Wanted

Wash dishes $1.50

Feed cat $.95

Mow lawn $3.50

Mop floors $1.25

Pick tomatoes $2.75

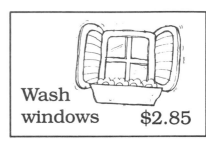
Wash windows $2.85

Use the Help Wanted poster above to help you find out how much you can earn by doing each set of jobs. Write the total amount for each set.

1. feed cat	1. wash dishes	1. wash windows	1. feed cat
2. pick tomatoes	2. mow lawn	2. mop floors	2. wash windows
3. wash dishes	3. wash windows	3. mow lawn	3. mop floors

1. pick tomatoes	1. feed cat	1. pick tomatoes	1. mop floors
2. wash windows	2. wash dishes	2. wash windows	2. pick tomatoes
3. feed cat	3. mop floors	3. mow lawn	3. wash windows

So Many Choices!

Name _____

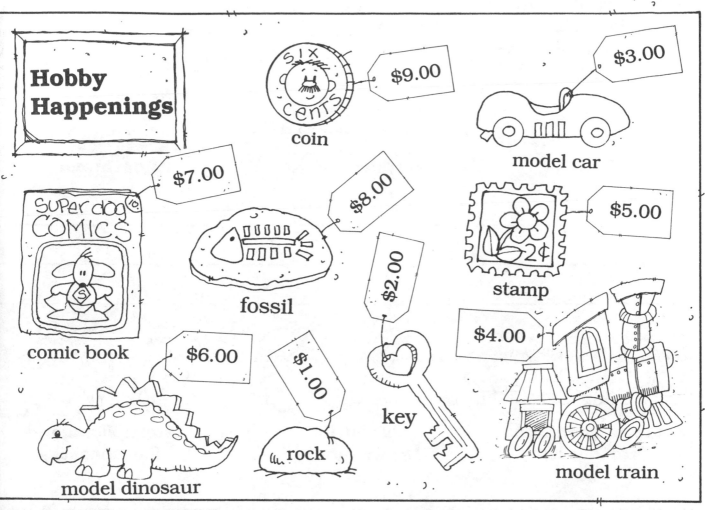

Hobby Happenings

coin — $9.00

model car — $3.00

comic book — $7.00 (Super dog COMICS)

fossil — $8.00

stamp — $5.00

$2.00

key

$4.00

model dinosaur — $6.00

rock — $1.00

model train

You want to buy 3 **different** items in the hobby store. You have $16.00. Write all the different combinations of items you can buy using the entire $16.00.

1. _____   1. _____   1. _____   1. _____

2. _____   2. _____   2. _____   2. _____

3. _____   3. _____   3. _____   3. _____

1. _____   1. _____   1. _____   1. _____

2. _____   2. _____   2. _____   2. _____

3. _____   3. _____   3. _____   3. _____

Exhibiting Native American Heritage

Name _____

Read the words in the Word Bank. Write them on the lines under the correct regional heading.

Plains

Northwest Coast

Southwest

_____

_____

_____

Eastern Woodlands (northeast)

California – Intermountain

Eastern Woodlands (southeast)

_____

_____

_____

Word Bank

beaded necklace	buffalo-hide tepee	Cheyenne
buffalo-hide tepee	plank house	Mohawk
leather ball	Tlingit	Navajo
planting stick	Shoshoni	chickee
long house	Seminole	hogan
lacrosse racket	salmon spear	canoe

Proudly Praising Our Country

Name _____

	1	2	3	4	5	6	7	8
A								
B								
C								
D								

Cut out the pictures at the bottom of this page. Read the directions. Paste the pictures where they belong.

1. Go to **B4**. Paste the **Liberty Bell** here.

2. Go to **D5**. Paste **Fort Clatsop** here.

3. Go to **A3**. Paste **Mount Vernon** here.

4. Go to **D2**. Paste **Fort Knox** here.

5. Go to **C6**. Paste the **Constitution** here.

6. Go to **A1**. Paste the **Mayflower** here.

7. Go to **B8**. Paste **Independence Rock** here.

8. Go to **D7**. Paste **Fort McHenry** here.

Cut ✂

Liberty Bell | Fort Clatsop | Mount Vernon | Fort Knox | Constitution | Mayflower | Independence Rock | Fort McHenry

"Time"-ly Toy Gifts

Name _____

Use the time line to answer the questions.

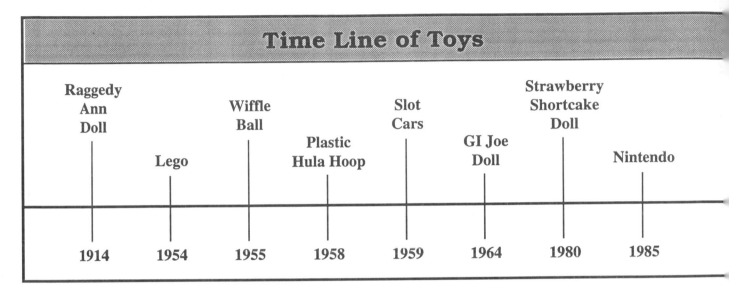

Time Line of Toys

Raggedy Ann Doll — 1914
Lego — 1954
Wiffle Ball — 1955
Plastic Hula Hoop — 1958
Slot Cars — 1959
GI Joe Doll — 1964
Strawberry Shortcake Doll — 1980
Nintendo — 1985

1. When did Nintendo first sell? _____

2. Could you play a game with a Wiffle Ball in 1940? _____

3. What new toy was sold in 1964? _____

4. In what year were plastic Hula Hoops first sold? _____

5. How many years passed between the first Raggedy Ann Doll and the first GI Joe Doll? _____

6. What toys were invented during the 1950's? _____

_____

7. How many toys on the time line were invented in the 1970's? _____

8. Could you have played with a plastic Hula Hoop in 1960? _____

9. In what year was the Strawberry Shortcake Doll first sold? _____

10. What new toy was first sold in 1954? _____

It's Time to Eat

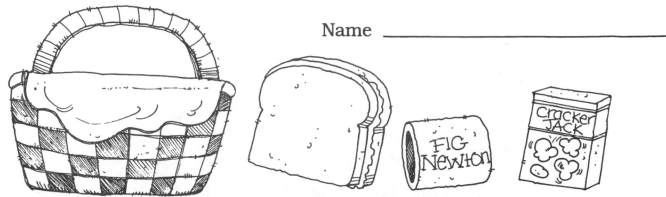

Name _____

Cut out the pictures at the bottom of this page. Follow the clues to paste them where they belong on the time line.

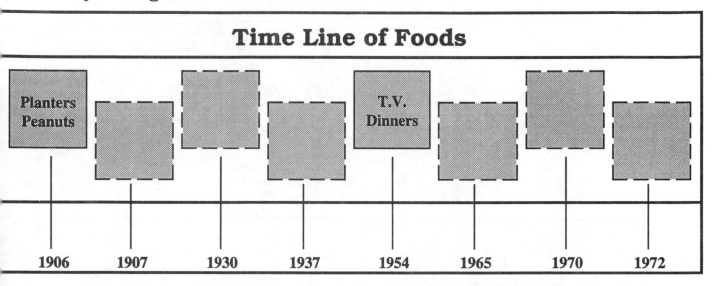

Time Line of Foods

Planters Peanuts				T.V. Dinners			
1906	1907	1930	1937	1954	1965	1970	1972

1. You could begin to eat Corn Flakes for breakfast 1 year after you could munch on Planters Peanuts.

2. Twinkies were first sold 23 years after Corn Flakes and 7 years before Spam.

3. You could top your favorite piece of pie with Cool Whip 35 years after you first tasted Twinkies.

4. A quick dinner could be made with Hamburger Helper two years before one could be made with Tuna Helper.

Cut -

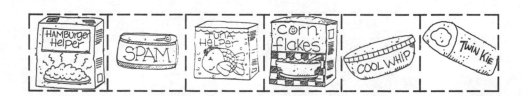

Build a Community

Name _____

Cut out the pictures at the bottom of this page. Read the directions. Paste the pictures where they belong.

1. Place the school **west** of the house and **east** of the row of trees.

2. Place the train at the **southwest** edge of the railroad tracks.

3. Place the Police Station **west** of the Train Station and **east** of the train.

4. Place the Grocery Store **east** of the house and **south** of the rising sun.

5. Place the Bank **north** of the train.

6. Place the Fire House **south** of the Grocery Store and **east** of the Train Station.

Cut ✂ -

Answer Key

File Folders
Social Studies Activities
Grades 2-3

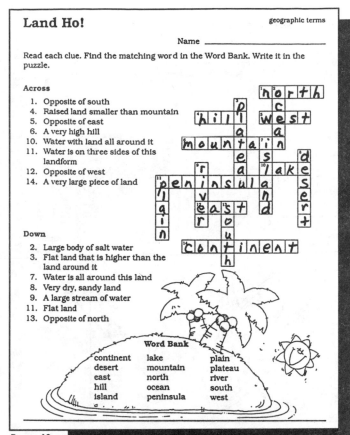

Land Ho!
geographic terms

Name _____

Read each clue. Find the matching word in the Word Bank. Write it in the puzzle.

Across

1. Opposite of south
4. Raised land smaller than mountain
5. Opposite of east
6. A very high hill
10. Water with land all around it
11. Water is on three sides of this landform
12. Opposite of west
14. A very large piece of land

Down

2. Large body of salt water
3. Flat land that is higher than the land around it
7. Water is all around this land
8. Very dry, sandy land
9. A large stream of water
11. Flat land
13. Opposite of north

Word Bank

continent   lake   plain
desert   mountain   plateau
east   north   river
hill   ocean   south
island   peninsula west

Page 63

Naturally Resourceful
natural resources

Name _____

Word Bank

bathe in   fishing   boating
fill a pool   motor oil   glass
maple syrup   plastic cups   lumber
paper plates   scissors   paint
sawdust   soak clothes   salt
wooden benches comic books   surfing

Write the words on the correct picture to show how each natural resource is used for.

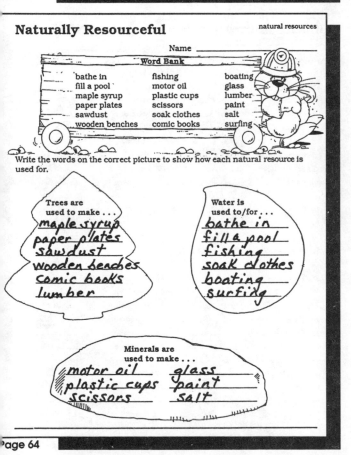

Trees are used to make . . .
maple syrup
paper plates
sawdust
wooden benches
comic books
lumber

Water is used to/for . . .
bathe in
fill a pool
fishing
soak clothes
boating
surfing

Minerals are used to make . . .
motor oil   glass
plastic cups   paint
scissors   salt

Page 64

How Far Is It?
measuring distance

Name _____

Use your ruler to measure each distance on the map. Then use the letters on the tires and your answers to solve the message at the bottom of the page.

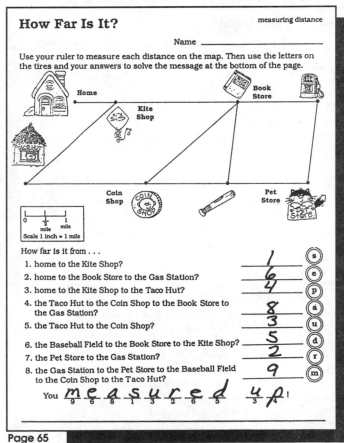

Scale 1 inch = 1 mile

How far is it from . . .

1. home to the Kite Shop?   1   (s)
2. home to the Book Store to the Gas Station?   6   (e)
3. home to the Kite Shop to the Taco Hut?   4   (p)
4. the Taco Hut to the Coin Shop to the Book Store to the Gas Station?   8   (a)
5. the Taco Hut to the Coin Shop?   3   (u)
6. the Baseball Field to the Book Store to the Kite Shop?   5   (d)
7. the Pet Store to the Gas Station?   2   (r)
8. the Gas Station to the Pet Store to the Baseball Field to the Coin Shop to the Taco Hut?   9   (m)

You m e a s u r e d   u p
     9 6 8 1 3 2 6 5   3 4

Page 65

---

77   IF8582 File Folder Social Studies Activities

Answer Key

"Good Service" Delivery
goods and services

Name _____

Read each word. If it names an occupation that provides goods, mark G on the word. If it names an occupation that provides a service, mark S on the word. Then draw a line to show where three answers are the same in a row.

G	S	S
television salesperson	veterinarian	zookeeper

S	G	S
receptionist	pizza parlor owner	lawyer

S	S	G
crossing guard	school bus driver	kite manufacturer

S	S	G
actor	plumber	toy maker

S	G	S
firefighter	music store owner	principal

G	G	S
shoe salesperson	cook	babysitter

Page 66

Selecting Supplies
wants and needs

Name _____

Read each word in the Word Bank. If a word names a **need**, write it on the sack of flour. If a word names a **want**, write it on the pickle barrel.

Word Bank
videotape milk bracelet
kite soda pop bed candy bar
soccer ball home backpack
vegetables balloon fruit
bread coat hat

Want
videotape
bracelet
kite
soda pop
candy bar
soccer ball
backpack
balloon

Need
milk
bed
home
vegetables
fruit
bread
coat
hat

Page 67

Seeking the Sights
geography

Name _____

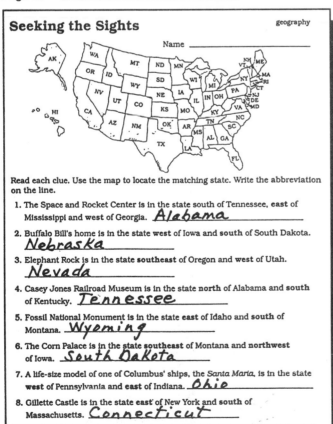

Read each clue. Use the map to locate the matching state. Write the abbreviation on the line.

1. The Space and Rocket Center is in the state south of Tennessee, **east of** Mississippi and west of Georgia. *Alabama*

2. Buffalo Bill's home is in the state west of Iowa and south of South Dakota. *Nebraska*

3. Elephant Rock is in the state **southeast** of Oregon and west of Utah. *Nevada*

4. Casey Jones Railroad Museum is in the state **north** of Alabama and **south** of Kentucky. *Tennessee*

5. Fossil National Monument is in the state **east** of Idaho and **south** of Montana. *Wyoming*

6. The Corn Palace is in the state **southeast** of Montana and **northwest** of Iowa. *South Dakota*

7. A life-size model of one of Columbus' ships, the *Santa Maria*, is in the state **west** of Pennsylvania and **east** of Indiana. *Ohio*

8. Gillette Castle is in the state **east** of New York and south of Massachusetts. *Connecticut*

Page 68

Briefly Addressed
state name abbreviations

Name _____

Write the postal abbreviation for each state.

1. Washington	WA	26. Oregon	OR
2. California	CA	27. Idaho	ID
3. Nevada	NV	28. Arizona	AZ
4. Montana	MT	29. Wyoming	WY
5. Utah	UT	30. Colorado	CO
6. New Mexico	NM	31. North Dakota	ND
7. South Dakota	SD	32. Nebraska	NE
8. Kansas	KS	33. Oklahoma	OK
9. Texas	TX	34. Minnesota	MN
10. Iowa	IA	35. Missouri	MO
11. Arkansas	AR	36. Louisiana	LA
12. Wisconsin	WI	37. Illinois	IL
13. Mississippi	MS	38. Indiana	IN
14. Ohio	OH	39. Kentucky	KY
15. Tennessee	TN	40. Alabama	AL
16. Pennsylvania	PA	41. New York	NY
17. Vermont	VT	42. New Hampshire	NH
18. Maine	ME	43. Massachusetts	MA
19. Rhode Island	RI	44. Connecticut	CT
20. New Jersey	NJ	45. Delaware	DE
21. Maryland	MD	46. Virginia	VA
22. West Virginia	WV	47. North Carolina	NC
23. South Carolina	SC	48. Georgia	GA
24. Florida	FL	49. Michigan	MI
25. Alaska	AK	50. Hawaii	HI

Page 69

Answer Key

Earnings Add Up!
earning money

Name _____

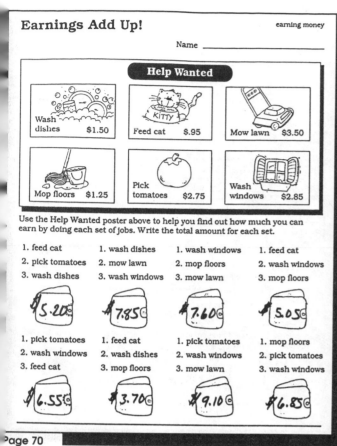

Help Wanted

Wash dishes $1.50	Feed cat $.95	Mow lawn $3.50
Mop floors $1.25	Pick tomatoes $2.75	Wash windows $2.85

Use the Help Wanted poster above to help you find out how much you can earn by doing each set of jobs. Write the total amount for each set.

1. feed cat	1. wash dishes	1. wash windows	1. feed cat
2. pick tomatoes	2. mow lawn	2. mop floors	2. wash windows
3. wash dishes	3. wash windows	3. mow lawn	3. mop floors
$5.20	$7.85	$7.60	$5.05

1. pick tomatoes	1. feed cat	1. pick tomatoes	1. mop floors
2. wash windows	2. wash dishes	2. wash windows	2. pick tomatoes
3. feed cat	3. mop floors	3. mow lawn	3. wash windows
$6.55	$3.70	$9.10	$6.85

Page 70

So Many Choices!
spending money

Name _____

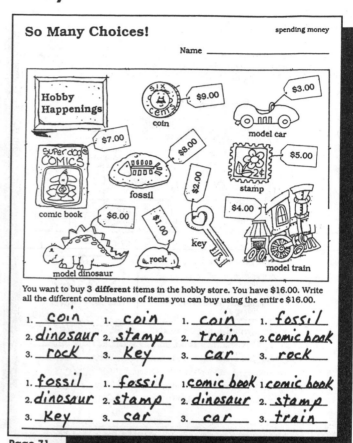

Hobby Happenings

coin $9.00 — model car $3.00 — $7.00 — $8.00 — stamp $5.00 — fossil — $2.00 — $4.00 — comic book $6.00 — $1.00 — key — rock — model dinosaur — model train

You want to buy **3 different** items in the hobby store. You have $16.00. Write all the different combinations of items you can buy using the entire $16.00.

1. coin	1. coin	1. coin	1. fossil
2. dinosaur	2. stamp	2. train	2. comic book
3. rock	3. key	3. car	3. rock

1. fossil	1. fossil	1. comic book	1. comic book
2. dinosaur	2. stamp	2. dinosaur	2. stamp
3. key	3. car	3. car	3. train

Page 71

Exhibiting Native American Heritage
Native Americans

Name _____

Read the words in the Word Bank. Write them on the lines under the correct regional heading.

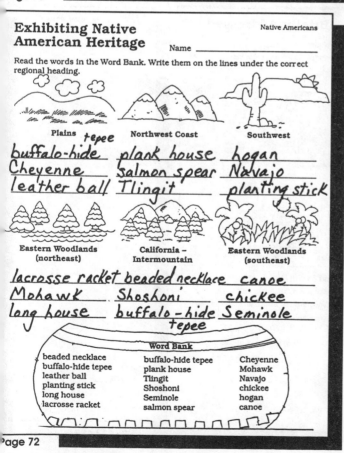

Plains
buffalo-hide tepee
Cheyenne
leather ball

Northwest Coast
plank house
salmon spear
Tlingit

Southwest
hogan
Navajo
planting stick

Eastern Woodlands (northeast)
lacrosse racket
Mohawk
long house

California – Intermountain
beaded necklace
Shoshoni
buffalo-hide tepee

Eastern Woodlands (southeast)
canoe
chickee
Seminole

Word Bank

beaded necklace	buffalo-hide tepee	Cheyenne
buffalo-hide tepee	plank house	Mohawk
leather ball	Tlingit	Navajo
planting stick	Shoshoni	chickee
long house	Seminole	hogan
lacrosse racket	salmon spear	canoe

Page 72

Proudly Praising Our Country
United States symbols and places

Name _____

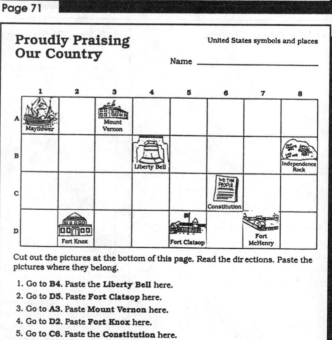

Cut out the pictures at the bottom of this page. Read the directions. Paste the pictures where they belong.

1. Go to B4. Paste the **Liberty Bell** here.
2. Go to D5. Paste **Fort Clatsop** here.
3. Go to A3. Paste **Mount Vernon** here.
4. Go to D2. Paste **Fort Knox** here.
5. Go to C6. Paste the **Constitution** here.
6. Go to A1. Paste the *Mayflower* here.
7. Go to B8. Paste **Independence Rock** here.
8. Go to D7. Paste **Fort McHenry** here.

Cut ✂

Page 73

Answer Key

"Time"-ly Toy Gifts

time line

Name _____

Use the time line to answer the questions.

Time Line of Toys

Raggedy Ann Doll		Wiffle Ball		Slot Cars		Strawberry Shortcake Doll	
	Lego		Plastic Hula Hoop		GI Joe Doll		Nintendo
1914	1954	1955	1958	1959	1964	1980	1985

1. When did Nintendo first sell? __1985__
2. Could you play a game with a Wiffle Ball in 1940? __no__
3. What new toy was sold in 1964? __GI Joe__
4. In what year were plastic Hula Hoops first sold? __1958__
5. How many years passed between the first Raggedy Ann Doll and the first GI Joe Doll? __50__
6. What toys were invented during the 1950's? __Lego, SlotCars, Wiffle Ball, Plastic Hula Hoop__
7. How many toys on the time line were invented in the 1970's? __none__
8. Could you have played with a plastic Hula Hoop in 1960? __yes__
9. In what year was the Strawberry Shortcake Doll first sold? __1980__
10. What new toy was first sold in 1954? __Lego__

Page 74

It's Time to Eat

making a time line

Name _____

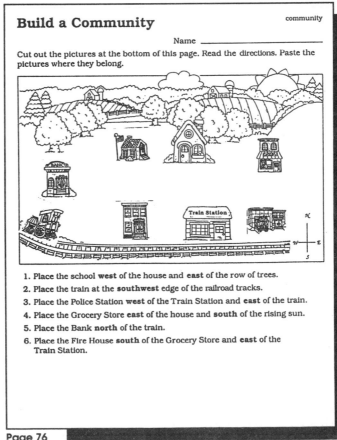

Cut out the pictures at the bottom of this page. Follow the clues to paste them where they belong on the time line.

Time Line of Foods

Planters Peanuts	Corn Flakes	Twinkies	SPAM	T.V. Dinners	COOL WHIP	Hamburger Helper	
1906	1907	1930	1937	1954	1965	1970	1972

1. You could begin to eat Corn Flakes for breakfast 1 year after you could munch on Planters Peanuts.
2. Twinkies were first sold 23 years after Corn Flakes and 7 years before Spam.
3. You could top your favorite piece of pie with Cool Whip 35 years after you first tasted Twinkies.
4. A quick dinner could be made with Hamburger Helper two years before one could be made with Tuna Helper.

Page 75

Build a Community

community

Name _____

Cut out the pictures at the bottom of this page. Read the directions. Paste the pictures where they belong.

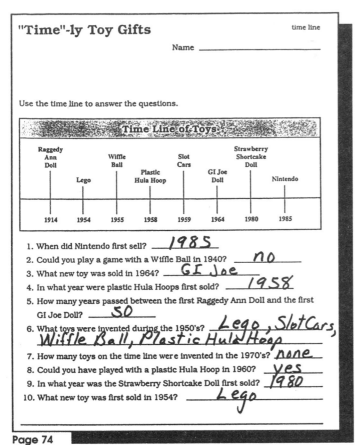

1. Place the school **west** of the house and **east** of the row of trees.
2. Place the train at the **southwest** edge of the railroad tracks.
3. Place the Police Station **west** of the Train Station and **east** of the train.
4. Place the Grocery Store **east** of the house and **south** of the rising sun.
5. Place the Bank **north** of the train.
6. Place the Fire House **south** of the Grocery Store and **east** of the Train Station.

Page 76

IF8582 File Folder Social Studies Activitie